Seven Is Magic

THEODORE CLYMER · VIRGINIA W. JONES

CONSULTANTS

ROGER W. SHUY • E. PAUL TORRANCE

LINGUISTICS CREATIVITY

READING 360 READING 360 READING 360 READING 360

GINN

GINN AND COMPANY

A XEROX COMPANY

Acknowledgments

Grateful acknowledgment is made to the following authors and publishers for permission to use and adapt copyrighted materials:

Child Life magazine for the poem "Little Satellite," by Jane W. Krows. From *Child Life,* Copyright 1961.

LeRoy Condie for "White Horse," adapted from *A Story of the Grand Canyon*.

Thomas Y. Crowell Company for "Paddy the Penguin," adapted from *Paddy the Penguin,* by Paul Galdone. Copyright © 1959 by Paul Galdone. Thomas Y. Crowell Company, New York, publishers.

The Curtis Publishing Company for "Lucy's Smile," adapted from "Lucy Couldn't Smile" by Margaret Baur. Adapted by special permission from *Jack and Jill* magazine, © 1965, The Curtis Publishing Company; and for "The Little Boy with the Big Name," adapted from "The Little Boy with the Big Name" by Dorothy Binder. Adapted by special permission from *Jack and Jill* magazine, © 1966, The Curtis Publishing Company.

Follett Publishing Company for the poem "Motor Cars," by Rowena Bennett. Reprinted from *Songs From Around A Toadstool Table,* copyright © 1967 by Rowena Bennett. Used by permission of Follett Publishing Company.

Harcourt, Brace & World, Inc., for the poems "Curiosity," and "The Gnome," from *Windy Morning,* copyright, 1953, by Harry Behn. Reprinted by permission of Harcourt, Brace & World, Inc.; and for the poem "Snow Toward Evening," by Melville Cane. Copyright, 1926, by Harcourt, Brace & World, Inc.; renewed, 1954, by Melville Cane. Reprinted from his volume, *So That It Flower,* by permission of the publishers.

Harper & Row, Publishers for permission to use the poem "Apartment Houses" from *I Live in a City* by James S. Tippett. Copyright 1927 Harper & Brothers.

Humpty Dumpty's Magazine for "Pork Chops and Applesauce," adapted from "Pork Chops and Applesauce" by Dorothy Levenson, (November, 1965); for "Night Light," adapted from "The Old Woman and Her Pets" by Ruth Liebers, (September, 1965); for "The Boy and the Wolf," adapted from "The Boy and the Wolf" by Freya Littledale, (April, 1965). All stories first appeared in *Humpty Dumpty's Magazine*.

Friede Orleans Joffe for the poem "The Lost Balloon." from *Funday* by Ilo Orleans. Reprinted by permission of Friede Orleans Joffe.

J. B. Lippincott Company for the poem "A Letter Is a Gypsy Elf," from *For Days and Days* by Annette Wynne. Copyright 1919, 1947 by Annette Wynne. Published by J. B. Lippincott Company.

Lothrop, Lee and Shepard Co., Inc., for "Grandfather and I" by Helen E. Buckley, reprinted by permission of Lothrop, Lee & Shepard Co., Inc. *Grandfather and I* by Helen E. Buckley, copyright © 1959, by Lothrop, Lee & Shepard Co., Inc.

Harold Ober Associates, Inc., for the poem "City," from *The Langston Hughes Reader* by Langston Hughes. Copyright © 1958 by Langston Hughes. Reprinted by permission of Harold Ober Associates, Inc.

Odille Ousley for her story "The New Fence," which has been adapted for this book.

Martha K. Tippett for the poem "Apartment Houses," from *I Live in a City* by James S. Tippett, copyright 1927, by Harper & Brothers.

Mabel Watts for "Three in a Tree," adapted from "Three in a Tree." Published originally in *Humpty Dumpty's* magazine, (February, 1962). Adapted by permission of Mabel Watts.

HOME OFFICE, BOSTON, MASSACHUSETTS 02117

Contents

Freckles
Carlo
Lucy
Pat
Ted
1
PEOPLE WE KNOW

Freckles

"Freckles! Freckles!" said Carlo.

"You stop it, Carlo," said Mike.
"My name is not Freckles.
My name is Mike, Mike Parks."

"You can't stop me!" said Carlo.
"Freckles! Freckles!"

Mike looked at his face.
He didn't like what he saw.
His face did have freckles!
And Mike didn't like his freckles at all.

"Names! Names!" Mike said.
"Why do people have to make up names?
I can't help all the freckles!"

Mike made a face.

Mike saw Dad's shaving cream.

"Maybe this shaving cream will help," said Mike.

He put some on his face.

The freckles didn't go away.

Then Mike put something green on his face.

When he looked up, his freckles looked back at him.

"Dad's shaving cream didn't help," said Mike.

"All of this will not help.

Freckles! I do NOT like freckles!"

Dad came in.

"What are you doing?" he asked.

"I don't like my frecklcs, Dad," said Mike.

"The boys call me names.

I put shaving cream and some of this on my face.

But the freckles did not go away.

I don't want the boys to call me Freckles."

"I know, Mike," said Dad.

"When I was a little boy,
I was a shorty.

The other boys liked to call me
Shorty—Shorty Parks."

"Shorty Parks?" asked Mike.

"But Dad, you aren't a shorty now!

You aren't a shorty at all."

"I know," said Dad.

"But sometimes boys like
to make fun of other boys.

Sometimes people say things we don't like."

Mike had to smile.

He didn't like to be called Freckles.

But his dad had put up with Shorty—
Shorty Parks!

"Thanks, Dad," said Mike
with a smile.

He whistled and walked away.

Apartment Houses

Apartment houses on our street
Stand side by side.
Some of them are narrow,
Some are wide.

Some of them are low,
Some are high;
Some of them have towers
That reach into the sky.

All of them have windows,
Oh, so many!
There is not one house
That doesn't have any.

James S. Tippett

PAT'S SCHOOL PICTURE

"Where did you get all the pictures?" called Pat.

"I see pictures here of all of you, but I don't see mine!
Who took the pictures?"

"Miss White took the pictures when you were out of school," said Mike.

It was time to read, but Pat didn't look at his book.
He thought about the time he was out of school.
He thought about the school pictures.
Pat wanted his picture up too!

The following day Pat ran
all the way to school.

He had thought of a way
to get his picture up.

When Pat got to school, he said,
"Here, Miss White.
This is a picture my dad took.
He took it the day I was out of school.
I'm going to put it up
with the other pictures."

The children looked at Pat's picture.

"That's some picture, Pat," said Mike.

"What can we name it?" asked Miss White.

"We can call it PAT'S SCHOOL PICTURE," said Mike.

The children smiled.
They all liked
that name.

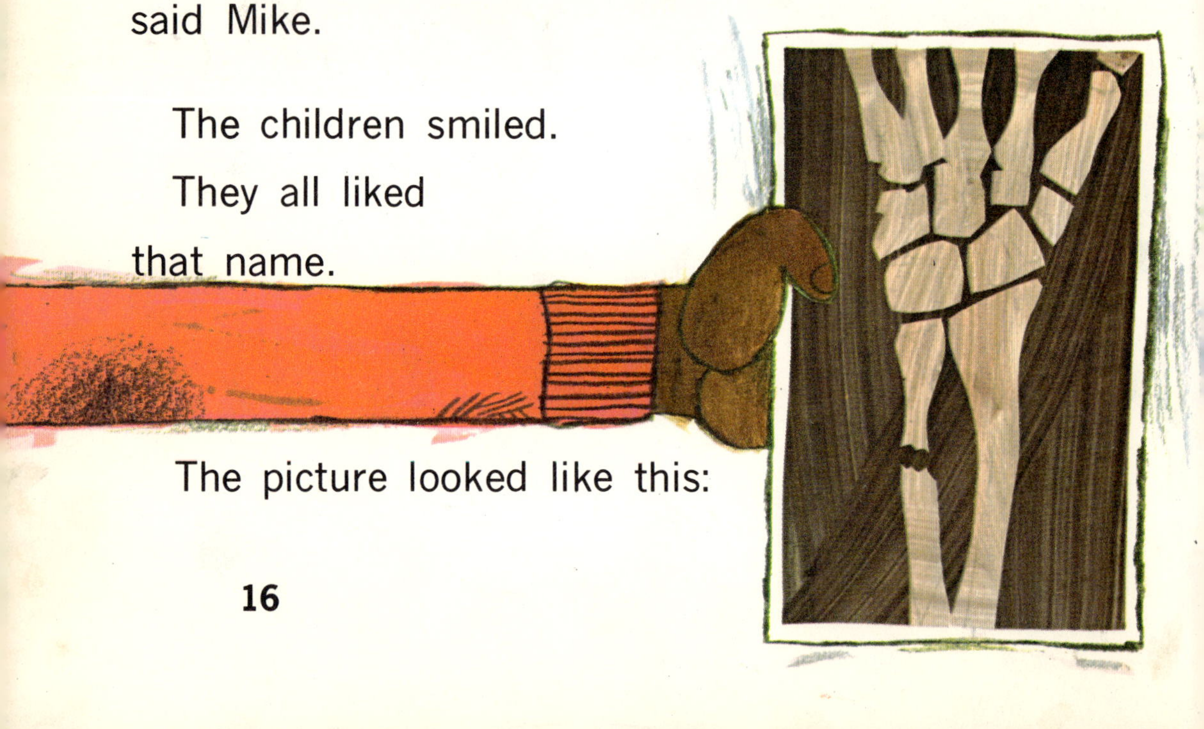

The picture looked like this:

LUCY'S SMILE

Lucy liked to smile.

People who lived on Lucy's street liked the way she smiled.

But a time came when Lucy didn't smile.

Lucy came down the street on her way to school.

"Hello, Lucy," called Mr. Cunningham.

Lucy waved, but she did not smile.

Mr. Cunningham thought, "Lucy waved, but I did not see her smile.

Where is Lucy's smile?"

Mrs. Dandy saw Lucy.

"Hello, Lucy," Mrs. Dandy called.

Lucy waved to Mrs. Dandy.
She did not smile.
"Well," thought Mrs. Dandy.
"Where is Lucy's smile?"

Lucy came to school.

Some children called, and Lucy waved back.

She did not smile at all.

The children looked at her in surprise.

"Where is Lucy's smile?" the children thought.

It was time to work.
Miss White asked Lucy to read.
Lucy walked up to Miss White
and said something to her.

"Lucy has a surprise for you,"
said Miss White.

Lucy smiled at all the children.
"Why, Lucy!" Miss White said.
"What a big smile!"

When the children looked at Lucy,
thcy smiled too.

Can you guess
why Lucy had not smiled?
What was
her surprise?

Lucy looked at her book,
but she wasn't reading it.

"Lucy," asked Miss White.
"Are you reading?"

Lucy wanted to hide her face.
"It's my birthday, Miss White,"
said Lucy. "I'm seven today!"

"A birthday today! Now I know why you are not reading," said Miss White.

"So you are seven today! Seven is magic, Lucy."

"Seven is magic?" asked Lucy.

"What's so magic about seven?"

"You will see," said Miss White.

At last it was time to go home.

All the way Lucy thought about her birthday.

"Why is seven magic?" she thought.

Lucy looked up.
"That's funny," she said.
"Here's my house . . .
77 Hill Street."

Lucy walked
up to her apartment.
"Seven here too,"
thought Lucy.
"I live in Apartment Seven.
But that can't
be magic."

Lucy went
into the apartment.
She had work to do.
"That's funny," she thought.
"Seven people will eat here.
But that can't be magic."

Mother and Dad and Lucy's four brothers came home.

The four boys had a surprise for Lucy.

It was for her birthday.

"A hamster!" said Lucy. "Thank you! Thank you! I like my hamster. She will make a good pet."

That night Lucy didn't want
to go to sleep.

"This is a birthday
to remember," she thought.

"But what can be the magic
in this birthday?"

Lucy thought about her four brothers
and her pet hamster.

She thought about Apartment Seven
at 77 Hill Street.

She thought about the seven people
who lived in this apartment.

"I remember what
Miss White said," thought Lucy.

"But what can be so magic
about all the sevens?"

At last Lucy went to sleep.

When it was time to get up,
Lucy went to look at the hamster.
"Mother! Dad! Come and see!
We have seven little hamsters!"

Mother and Dad came.
Lucy's four brothers came too.
"Look!" said Lucy.
"Look at all the little hamsters.
Seven IS magic!"

Ted and the Telephone

Ted was
on the telephone.

Dad said, "Hello, Ted.
Will you ask Mother to come for me?
Ask her to come to 5th Street at four.
Can you remember that?"

"I can remember," said Ted.
"5th Street at four!"

"Who was that?" asked Mother.

"It was Dad," said Ted.
"He wants you to come
to 4th Street at five."

At four o'clock
Dad went to 5th Street.
Mother did not come.
"Where can she be?"
thought Dad.

At five o'clock
Mother went to 4th Street.
Dad did not come.
"Where can he be?"
thought Mother.

When Mother and Dad got home, they called Ted.

"You have to remember," they said.

"When you answer the telephone, you have to remember what is said."

"I will," said Ted.

"I can answer the telephone, and I can remember too."

Grandmother called,
and Ted answered the telephone.

"Please ask Andy to go
to the store for me,"
said Grandmother.

"I want a can of fish and
four cans of milk.
Can you remember that?"

"I can remember," said Ted.
"You want a can of fish and
four cans of milk."

"Who was that?" asked Andy.
"It was grandmother,"
said Ted.
"She wants you
to go to the store for her.
You are to get four cans of fish
and a can of milk."

Andy went to the store
and then to Grandmother's house.

"What is this?" asked Grandmother.
"I wanted four cans of milk.
What do you think I will do
with all this fish?"

Andy smiled.
"That Ted!" he said.
"He thinks he can remember,
but he can't.
I will go back to the store
and get what you want."

When Andy got home,
he called Ted.

"You don't remember
what people say on the telephone,
Ted," he said.

"And you can't answer the telephone
when you can't remember.

I think I can help you.

Wait here."

When Andy came back,
this is what he had for Ted.

Who called?
What did they want?

Now Ted will remember!

Pork Chops and Applesauce

Down the street from Ted's house was a store.

Ted liked to go to the store for Grandmother.

He liked to look at all the boxes and cans.

And he liked Mr. King, the man who ran the store.

Ted saw Mr. King and waved to him.

"Hello, Ted," said Mr. King.
"Do you have time to help me?"

"Yes, I do," answered Ted.
"What can I do to help?"

"Come with me," said Mr. King.
"Take the pork chops, Ted.
Put them here with the others."

Ted got the pork chops
and put them with the others.
He liked helping Mr. King.
Then Ted remembered something.
He liked applesauce with pork chops.
Sometimes Mother forgot
to get the applesauce.

Ted thought, "Maybe other people forget it too.

I can get some cans of applesauce and put them with the pork chops.

Then other mothers will not forget."

Ted saw the gingerbread.

"This is something I like to eat too," he thought.

"Gingerbread is good with ice cream!

I will put the gingerbread with the ice cream."

Mr. King hadn't looked at what Ted was doing.

A woman asked for some applesauce.

Mr. King couldn't find it.

A freckle-faced boy asked,

"Where is the gingerbread?"

Mr. King looked, but he couldn't find it.

"What's going on here?" asked Mr. King.

"I can't find the food in my store!"

“Ted! Ted!” called Mr. King.
“What are you doing?
This is not right.
Why are you doing this?”

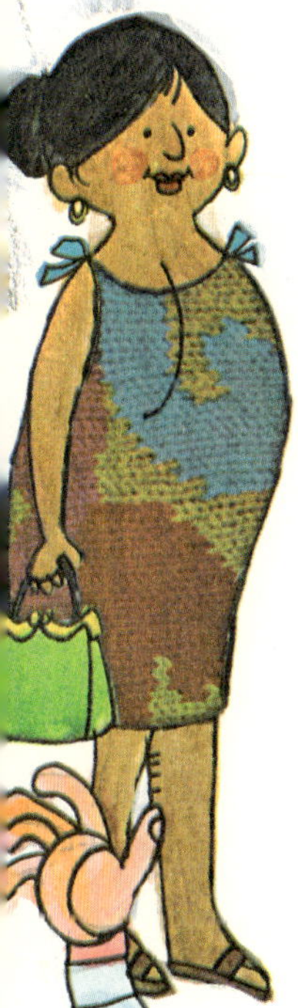

Ted looked at Mr. King.
He thought, “Maybe I wasn’t right to put the applesauce with the pork chops.
Maybe Mr. King will not let me work in the store.”

Mr. King looked at the people.
He saw big smiles on all the faces.

"It's all right, Mr. King," said the woman. "The boy helped me remember to get applesauce for my pork chops."

"And he helped me remember to get ice cream to go with my gingerbread," said the boy with the freckles.

Mr. King smiled. "It's all right, Ted," he said. "You did something for me, and something for the store too. You helped me remember that applesauce goes with pork chops!"

New Words
You Can Read and Use

smell	**chin**	**rice**	**cook**
smack	**chip**	**mice**	**hook**
smash	**chill**	**nice**	**took**
	chick	**race**	**shook**
	cheek	**lace**	**wool**
	chase	**place**	**foot**
		trace	

Look back at the new words.
Can you find a new word
to answer these questions?

What does Pat like to eat?

What will some dogs do when they see a cat?

If a glass fell from the table, what would it do?

What would look for bugs in the grass?

What could two boys run?

People You Know

Here are some of the people you met in your stories.

Read the following words.
Then look at the pictures.
Can you name the boy or girl
each word makes you think of ?

smile	**Dad**	**seven**
pork chops	**apartment**	**shaving cream**
birthday	**telephone**	**magic**
freckles	**picture**	**school**

In what ways are these people
like boys and girls you know ?
Do you like Mike, Lucy, Pat,
or Ted the best ? Why ?

PEOPLE WE'D
LIKE TO
KNOW

The School Fair

Bill whistled and walked down the steps of Anders School.

This was one day when the school did not look like a school at all.

It was the day of the school fair.

Mr. Ball had come to do some magic at the fair.

Bozo was there to make the children smile.

There was something for Bill to do at the fair too.

He would be helping Mr. Mays with the balloons.

"Right this way!" Bill called.

"Balloons! Balloons!

Get your balloons here!"

There was a balloon for every boy and every girl at Anders School.

Every balloon had a postcard with it.
The postcard said:

This balloon came to you from
the children at the Anders School.
Please mail the postcard back
to the school. We want to know
who you are and where you live.
Thank you

Mr. Mays let one balloon go.

Then he called to the children,
"Let the balloons go!"

The children thought about the people who would get the balloons.

Who could they be?

What fun it would be when the postcards came back in the mail!

The children could not wait!

Kay

A postcard came in the mail.
It was from a little girl named Kay.
It said:

I live in the woods.
My Dad is a lumberman.
I am mailing a surprise
for all the children at
the Anders School. Kay

Late that day
the surprise came.
It was a small yellow book.
Kay had made it
with her dad's help.
It was about the woods
and about lumbering.

Kay's Book

My Dad works here in the woods.
Every day he goes into the woods.
He tags the tall trees that are
to come down.

Men come along
with saws.
They cut down
the tall trees.
Other men come along
to cut the tall trees
into logs.

Big trucks go
into the woods.

The logs are put
onto the trucks.

Then the trucks take the logs
to the sawmill.

At the sawmill, the logs are put
into a log pond.

The logs that are to be cut go from
the pond into the sawmill.
The logs are cut into lumber.
Houses can be made
from this lumber.

Mr. Mays put Kay's small yellow book where all the children could see it.

"That was a good surprise," said Bill. "It would be fun to live in the woods like that. It would be fun to see a lumberman cut the tall trees into logs."

"Where do you think the other balloons went?" asked the children.

"I don't know," said Mr. Mays. "The other postcards will have to answer that."

A Balloon That Works

Far from the Anders School,
Mr. Towns was working with a balloon.
This balloon was not a toy.
This balloon was a weather balloon.
It would find out about the weather
far up in the sky.
Mr. Towns let the big weather balloon go.
In no time at all it was far up
over the trees.

All at once Mr. Towns saw something!

The big weather balloon was going up into the sky.

A little red balloon was on its way down from the sky.

The little red balloon had a postcard with it.

“Look at this!” Mr. Towns called to the other workers.

“Here’s a postcard from some children in a city far away.

They want to know who we are, and where we live.”

A worker smiled and said, “Why not hand that postcard over to me?

My boy Sandy can answer this.

He can let the children know about weather balloons and the work they do.”

This balloon came to you from
the children at the Anders School.
Please mail the postcard back
to the school. We want to know
Who you are and
ere you live.
Thank You

Dear Boys and Girls,

In a box under the balloon are weather instruments.

The instruments find out about the weather on the way into space.

There is a radio in the box too. The radio lets weathermen know about the weather far up in the sky.

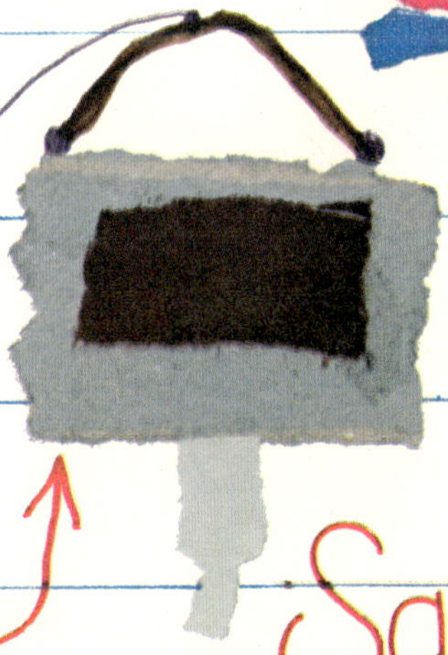

Sandy

MOTOR CARS

From a city window, 'way up high,
I like to watch the cars go by.
They look like burnished beetles, black,
That leave a little muddy track
Behind them as they slowly crawl.
Sometimes they do not move at all
But huddle close with hum and drone
As though they feared to be alone.
They grope their way through fog and night
With the golden feelers of their light.

Rowena Bennett

Sky House

Donna liked to be up
on the roof of the apartment house.
When the weather was fair,
she and her brother Don could play there.
Donna called the roof
"Sky House."

From the roof the children
could look far down on the city.
Big cars looked like little cars.
Little cars looked like ants.
Don said the trucks looked like toys.

Sometimes the children
came to Sky House at night.
Then they could see the lights of the city.
Don liked to see the lights on helicopters.
On and off, on and off, went the lights
in the night sky.

Donna liked to look off into space.
She thought the lights
in the night sky made magic pictures.

One day Don thought he saw a ship far away from Sky House.

Donna was about to look too, when she saw something.

"Don! Don!" she called.

"Come here right away.

I think I see a balloon!"

"It **is** a balloon!" said Don in surprise.

"And there's a postcard with it!"

Don and Donna read the postcard from the children at the Anders School.

"I know what we can say on the postcard," said Don.

"I know too," said Donna. "The children at this school would like to know about Sky House."

AIR MAIL

Nan was a little girl who could not go to school.

She couldn't run and hop and jump with the other children.

But every day school came to Nan!

Every day Miss Green came to help Nan with her schoolwork.

And every day Mr. Migs came with the mail.

Long before he came, Nan was waiting for him.

At the other houses Mr. Migs would put the mail in the boxes.

But not at Nan's house!

When mail came for Nan, Mr. Migs took it right to her.

Once a letter came from Nan's grandmother, who lived a long way off.

Other letters came from children who could go to school.

Before Mr. Migs went on, he would ask Nan about her schoolwork.

Nan would ask Mr. Migs about the weather.

One day Nan was doing her schoolwork for Miss Green.

As she was working, she saw Mr. Migs stop at the mailboxes on her street.

Nan waved, and Mr. Migs waved too.

Before long Nan finished her schoolwork.

"Maybe Mr. Migs has some mail for me today," thought Nan.

She looked up. There in the sky was a little red balloon.

Down, down it came.

"Mr. Migs!
Mr. Migs!"
Nan called.
"Please get that balloon for me."

Mr. Migs took the red balloon to her.

He and Nan read the postcard from Anders School.

"What a surprise!" said Nan.

"It's a surprise all right," said Mr. Migs.

"It's a funny way to get mail too. Guess you could say this postcard came by **air mail!**"

Mr. Migs smiled and went on with his work.

Nan went to work too. She had some air mail to answer.

A Letter Is a Gypsy Elf

A letter is a gypsy elf
It goes where I would go myself;
East or West or North, it goes,
Or South past pretty bungalows,
Over mountain, over hill,
Any place it must and will,
It finds good friends that live so far
You cannot travel where they are.

Annette Wynne

More about Balloons

This is the story of how balloons helped men find a way to fly.

A long, long time ago, some men were sitting around a fire.

They were looking at smoke going up into the air.

This made them think.

Could smoke make a bag go up too?

The men wanted to see.

They took a bag and held it over the smoke.

The warm air made the bag go up into the sky.

Then the men made a **big** bag.

Under this first balloon
they put a basket.

In the basket they put a pan.

In the pan was a fire.

The fire made the air warm.

The warm air
made the big balloon go up too!

The men made one more balloon.

It, too, had a basket and a pan.

There was a fire in the pan.

But this time there was something new.

In the basket were a duck, a rooster, and a sheep.

When the balloon went up into the sky, the animals went too.

It would be a long time before men could fly.

But balloons helped to find a way.

Can You Get to the Top?

Can you reach the balloon without missing a rung? First try one ladder. Then try another.

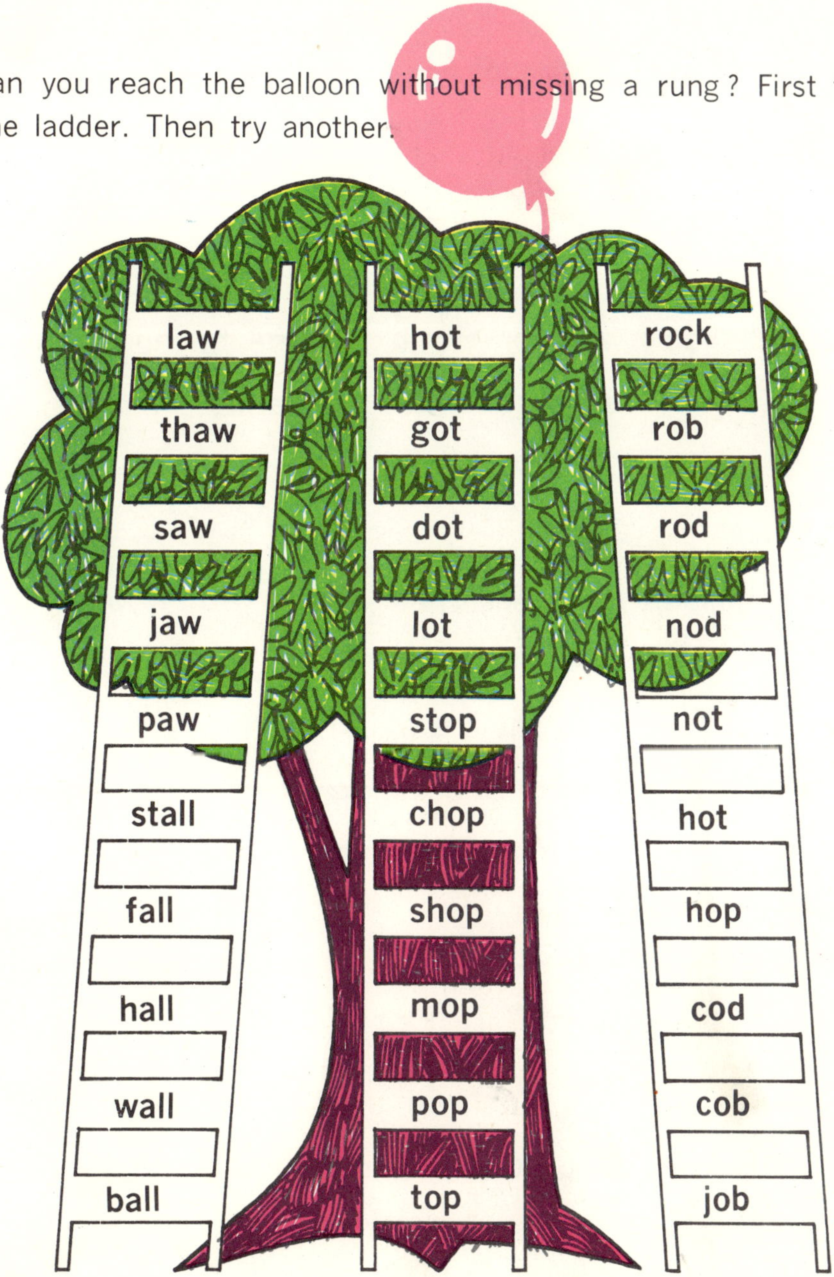

Try These Experiments

Would you like to know more about balloons?
Do these experiments.
Then think about what happens.

1. Fill a balloon with air. Then put the balloon into some water. Let it go. What happens?

2. Fill a balloon with air. Then rub it with wool. Hold it near your hand. What happens? Rub it again with wool. Hold it near the wall. What happens? Hold it near little bits of paper and move it back and forth over the paper. What happens?

3. Place two balloons filled with air near each other. Ask someone to rub one. You rub the other. Then step back and see what happens.

ALL AROUND THE CITY
3rd Street
3

CITY

In the morning the city
Spreads its wings
Making a song
Of stone that sings.

In the evening the city
Goes to bed
Hanging lights
About its head.

Langston Hughes

SIGHTS OF THE CITY

See the Sights!

See the Sights!

"See the sights!" called the tall man.

Every day the tall man came to 5th Street.

Every day he called, "See the sights! See the sights!"

One day Dan was walking on 5th Street.
The tall man was there.
He was calling, "See the sights!
See the sights!"
Dan saw a big sight-seeing bus stop on 5th Street.
There was a sign on the back of the bus.
The sign said, "See the Sights!
See the Sights!"

"What sights?
Where does that bus go?" Dan thought.

The next day Dan walked up to the tall man.

"I want to see the sights," he said. "When can I take the bus?"

"You're too late today," said the man. "Come back next Saturday. Saturday you can see the sights!"

The next Saturday Dan got on the big sight-seeing bus.

He was happy, for at last he was going to see the sights.

As the bus made its way down the street, a man talked to the people.

Dan did not know streets could go so many ways!

Some went up, and some went down.

Some went under other streets.

What fun it was seeing the many sights of the city!

Dan Sees the City

The bus made its first stop at a big red building.

Dan and the other people got off the bus.

They went up into the big red building.

What a sight this was!

Dan saw many, many animals in this building.

Where did animals like this come from?

When did they live?

Dan couldn't remember seeing animals so big before.

Next the bus came to the harbor.

Dan could see
big, **big** ships
and little, little boats.

Ships and boats,
big and little—
everywhere in the harbor.

He could see
men working
and men building.
He could see
men coming and going,
coming and going
everywhere.

The next stop was the city airport.

Dan saw a big jet take off.

What a noise it made!

Far up into
the blue sky went the jet.

Other jets took off
into the blue sky.

What a noise!

A man from the airport building talked to Dan and the others.

Dan asked about the big jet.

The man said it took people to a country far away.

"I want to go on a jet," said Dan.

"Maybe you will someday," the man said with a smile.

At last it was time to go home.

The bus took Dan and the others past apartments and stores.

It took them past cars and people.

When the bus came to 5th Street, Dan got off.

The other people on the bus could see a happy smile on his face.

They didn't know his name.

But they did know he was happy.

He had seen the sights of the city!

SNOW TOWARD EVENING

Suddenly the sky turned gray,
The day,
Which had been bitter and chill,
Grew soft and still.
Quietly
From some invisible blossoming tree
Millions of petals cool and white
Drifted and blew,
Lifted and flew,
Fell with the falling night.

Melville Cane

snow

Snow came to the city.

It came when the city was sleeping.

Softly, softly it came in the night.

White flakes fell on buildings and streets.

White, white flakes of snow on all the city.

All the city—soft and white in the night.

When daylight came, the snow was pretty and white.

But it did not stay pretty on the streets.

Before long workers came.

They took the snow away in trucks.

The policeman did not like working in the snow.

He could not keep all the cars going.

The people in the cars did not like the snow.

They didn't want to stay on the street all morning.

They wanted to keep going.

They wanted to get to work on time.

But the children liked the snow.
They liked to put on red boots.
They liked to walk in the snow.
They liked to make snowballs.

Red boots! White snowballs!
Red boots in the white snow!
White flakes on green trees!

What a pretty sight!

The children walked in the park.

The snow was soft and white on the trees.

"It looks pretty here in the park," a girl said softly.

The other children didn't answer.

They walked on to school in the soft white snow.

THE NEW FENCE

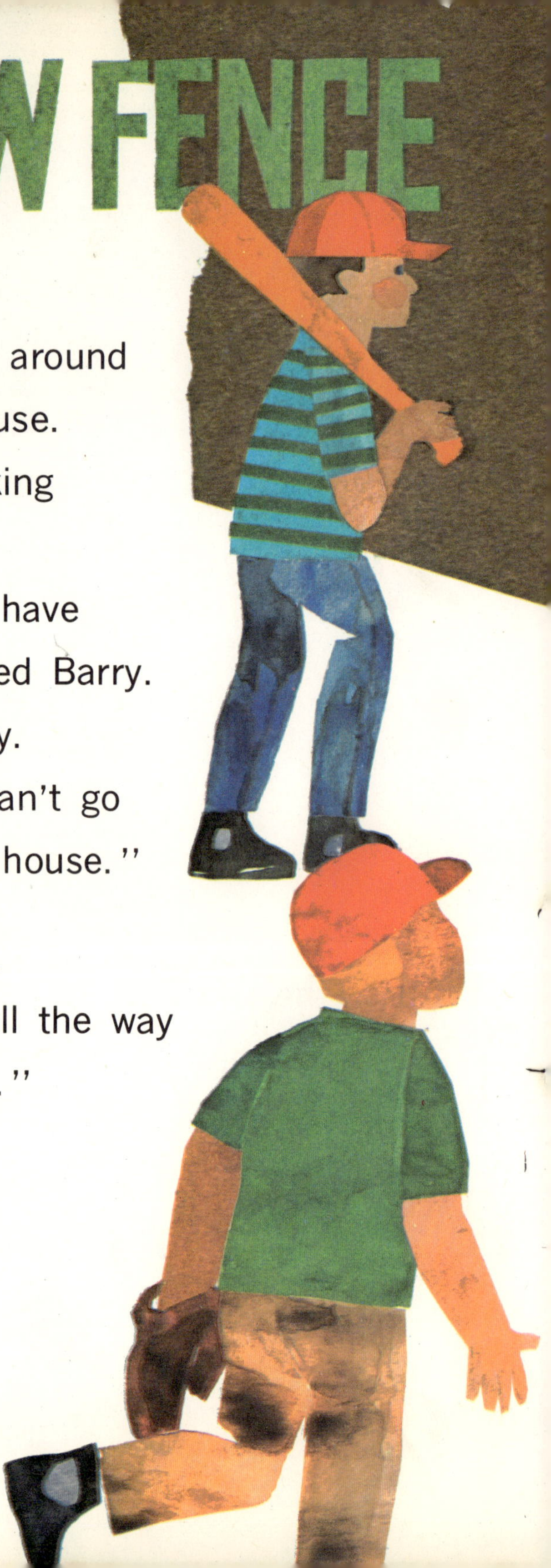

Pat and Barry walked around to the back of Pat's house.

They saw a man working on the back fence.

"Why do we have to have a new fence?" Pat asked Barry.

"I liked it the old way.

With a new fence, I can't go from my house to your house."

"I know," said Barry.

"We'll have to walk all the way around Park Street now."

"Don't you want the new fence?" called the workman.

"We don't want it at all," said Pat.
"We liked the old one."

"Now we have to walk all the way around Park Street," said Barry.

"I see," said the workman.
"That's too bad.
I know your mothers wanted a new fence.
I thought everyone would like a new one."

"Everyone but us," said Pat.
"We liked it the way it was."

Barry walked over
to the workman's truck.

"Come here, Pat," he called.

"Help me with this wood.
I have thought of something.
There's a way the man can fix
the fence.
We will not have to walk around it."

"I took this wood from your truck,"
Barry said to the workman.
"Would you do something for us?
Would you fix this wood like a seesaw?"

"A seesaw!" said Pat.
"He can't put a seesaw in a fence."

The workman smiled at Pat.
"Yes, I can," he said.
"I can fix this fence
in no time at all.
You will have a seesaw!"

The workman was right.
In no time at all the fence was fixed.
Pat was so surprised!

The boys liked having the seesaw.

What's more, now they liked having the new fence!

Everyone liked having a new fence.

Pat's mother and dad liked it.

Barry's mother and dad did too.

The workman was pleased, now that the boys liked it.

Yes, it was good to have a new fence!

FUN IN THE SUN

Sandy and her brother Sam walked down the street.

The sun made the city hot, too hot to run and play.

"Am I hot!" said Sam.

"Can we go to the park?"

"I don't want to walk that far in the hot sun," Sandy answered.

"Sam! Look, Sam!" Sandy called to her brother.

"It's Mr. Snow!"

The children ran to a little green car that had just come down the street.

"Hello, Sam. Hello, Sandy," said Mr. Snow.

"Thought you would like me to come and help you cool off on this hot day."

"Cool off! Who can cool off
when the sun is this hot?" Sam asked.
"Your name is cool,
but that's about all that is cool
in the city today."

Mr. Snow smiled at Sam.
"Look down the street," he said.

Sam and Sandy saw
a long red truck stop in the street.
A man in the truck waved
to the children.

"That man is going to make
you cool," said Mr. Snow.
"He will let the water run
in the street.
It will cool you off,
and wash the street too!"

Other children came out
to play in the wet street.
They splashed and splashed
in the cool water.

"Come down here, Sandy,"
called Sam.
"Come down and get splashed!"

But Sandy was not looking
at Sam or Mr. Snow or the other children.
She was looking up over the roof
of the apartment house.

"What a pretty sight!" she said.
Mr. Snow came over to look.
Some of the other children
came over too.

But not Sam.

He didn't want to look.

He liked being where he was with the cool water splashing over him.

It was good to be wet and cool on this hot day.

For Fun

Have you ever seen - - -

1. a bug on a rug with a mug?
2. chalk on the walk that could talk?
3. ten men in a pen with a hen?
4. a bun having fun in the sun?
5. a dog with a hog and a frog?
6. the top of a mop try to hop?

Read these sentences. The missing word will end with the same sounds as the name of the picture.

1. We will put a small 
   in this little white ____________.
2. You may find a 
   in the light of the ____________.
3. When you ride in a 
   you should put on a ____________.

Working with Letters and Words

Take away the b in bug. Put a d in its place. What word did you make? Now put another letter in place of the d. How many words can you make by taking away the first letter and putting another in its place?

Read the word that is next to each riddle. Then read the riddle. To find the answer to the riddle, take away the first letter of the word. Put a letter in its place.

fun

I shine.
I am warm.
You do not see me at night.
I am the ______________.

book

I am on a wall.
You can hang a picture on me.
You can hang a hat on me too.
I am a ______________.

fire

I go around and around.
You may put me on a car.
You may put me on a bike too.
I am a ______________.

What Is a City?

There are many cars and buses in a city.
You can look down on a city and see many tall buildings and the streets around them.

And you can see many things being made by many workers.

1. Do tall buildings make a city?
2. Do workers make a city?
3. Do cars and buses make a city?

What is a city, then?

WE LIKE TO LAUGH

Night Light

Mrs. Goody was a little old woman who lived in a little white house.

Three pets lived with her—a cat, a dog, and a bird.

When Mrs. Goody went to sleep, her three pets went to sleep.

When Mrs. Goody got up, the dog and the cat and the bird got up too.

It was a hot night, and Mrs. Goody couldn't sleep.

"Some cool water would be good," she thought.

Mrs. Goody got up and put on the light.

The bird saw the light.

"It's morning!" he sang.

"It is not morning," said Mrs. Goody. "Go back to sleep."

But the bird sang and sang.

The cat woke up.

"Good morning," he said in a sleepy way.

The dog woke up and thought it was morning too.

"No! No!" said Mrs. Goody.

"It is not morning.

Go back to sleep—all three of you!"

But the pets would not go back to sleep.

The noise woke Jill, and she woke her mother and father.

"Is it time to get up?" asked Jill.

"No, it is not," said her father. "Go back to sleep!"

Before long all the dogs on the street were up.

Cats ran about.

Birds sang in the trees.

At last a man who lived down the street called a policeman.

The policeman went to Mrs. Goody's house.

"What's going on?" he asked.

"My three pets woke up and thought it was morning," said Mrs. Goody.

"Now they will not go back to sleep.
What can I do?"

"Why did they get up at all?" asked the policeman.

"I put on the light to get some water," said Mrs. Goody.

"The light woke up the bird.
The bird woke up the cat.
The cat woke up the dog.
The noise woke up all the people."

The policeman laughed.

"Put out the light!" he said.

"Thank you, I will," said Mrs. Goody.

And she laughed too.

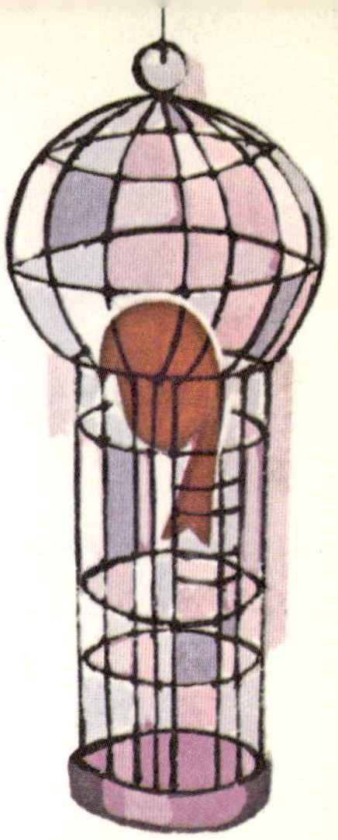

The old woman put out the light.

Her pets went back to sleep.

So did all the other animals on the street.

So did all the people.

And at last, so did Mrs. Goody.

Mr. Harvey's Hat

Mr. Harvey was so pleased with his new hat!
He walked out of his apartment house
and on down the street.
"My, my!
What a wind!
In this wind my new hat may not—"

With that off went Mr. Harvey's hat.

The wind had made the hat fly down the street.

"Stop! Stop!" Mr. Harvey called.

But the wind blew and blew.

It made the new hat fly on and on down the street.

Mr. Harvey's hat blew far, far away.

That day a farmer had come into the city in his truck.

Now he was going home.

As the truck came to a stoplight, Mr. Harvey's hat came flying down.

The new hat blew right into the farmer's truck.

Before long the truck was on its way once more.

And so was Mr. Harvey's hat!

The truck went away from the buildings of the city.

It went far out into the country.

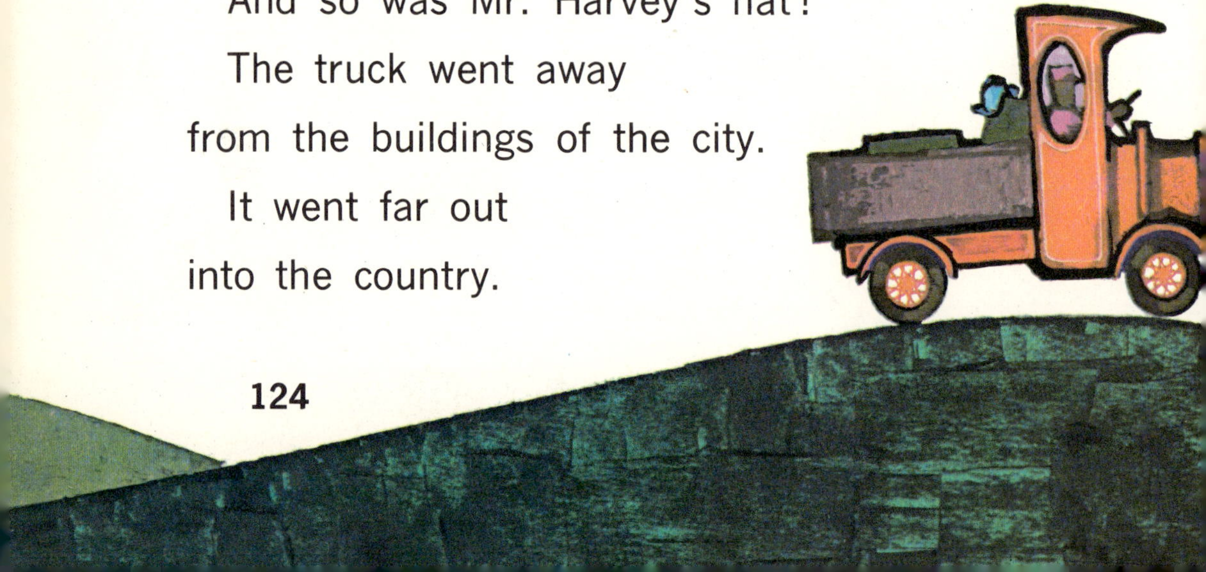

At last the truck came to a stop
in a cool barn.

A big blackbird looked down
from the top of the barn.

He could see the top of Mr. Harvey's hat
in the back of the truck.

"A hat!" thought the blackbird.

"I know something I can do with that!"

The blackbird took the hat
from the truck.

In no time at all
he was flying out of the barn
and over to the farmer's scarecrow.

He put the hat on top
of the scarecrow.

"Now I will know the farmer
from the scarecrow," said the blackbird.

He smiled as he thought of the trick
he had played on the farmer.

The next Saturday Mr. and Mrs. Harvey went for a ride.

Mr. Harvey's green car
left the tall buildings
and apartment houses of the city.

Soon Mr. and Mrs. Harvey
were far out in the country.

"Look over there," said Mrs. Harvey.

"Look at that funny scarecrow
in the farmer's garden.

He has on a hat like yours!"

Mr. Harvey stopped the car.

He looked at the hat

on top of the scarecrow.

"That looks just like—

but it couldn't be!

How could my new hat get out here?"

Then, without waiting for an answer, Mr. Harvey smiled.

"That is not my hat—
not my hat at all," he said.

"Let's keep going.
It's a good day for a ride
in the country!"

The Little Boy with the Big Name

The little boy
on the white fence was unhappy.

It was his name that made him unhappy.

Bradford Underwood Timothy Charles Hoppenpopper.

How would you like to have a long name like his?

"Why can't I have a name like other boys?" he thought.

He wanted to leave out some of his names.

But he couldn't leave out Hoppenpopper, for this was his last name.

Great-grandfather's name was Charles.

He couldn't leave out that name.

Grandfather's name was Timothy, so he couldn't leave out Grandfather's name.

Underwood had been Mother's name, so he couldn't leave out Underwood.

And he couldn't leave out Bradford, for that was his dad's name.

"What can I do?" thought the boy.

A wise old owl was in the tree over the white fence.

The owl was so wise, he could read the thoughts of the unhappy boy.

"I can help you,"
said Wise Old Owl.

"How can you help me?" asked the boy.
"I know you are wise,
but what can you do about my name?"

"Do as I say," said Wise Old Owl.
"Go home and get some paper.
Put down on the paper the first letters
of all your names.
Then you will have a new name."
Bradford Underwood Timothy Charles
Hoppenpopper couldn't wait to see
his new name.

He jumped down from the fence and ran all the way home.

One at a time, he put down on paper the first letters of all his names.

Then Bradford Underwood Timothy Charles Hoppenpopper smiled a big smile.

Do you know what the letters on the paper said?

Now .... has a new name, and he is not unhappy at all!

Curiosity

Tell me, tell me everything!
What makes it Winter
And then Spring?
Which are the children
Butterflies?
Why do people keep
Winking their eyes?
Where do birds sleep?
Do bees like to sting?
Tell me, tell me please, everything!

Tell me, tell me, I want to know!
What makes leaves grow
In the shapes they grow?
Why do goldfish
Keep chewing? and rabbits
Warble their noses?
Just from habits?
Where does the wind
When it goes away go?
Tell me! or don't even grown-ups know?

Harry Behn

Three in a Tree

THREE FRIENDS

An eagle, a cat, and a pig lived in a tree in the woods.

Eagle lived at the top of the tree.

Cat lived under Eagle.

Pig lived under Cat.

They liked to live this way.

Three in a tree!

When Eagle wanted something, he would call down to Cat.

When Cat wanted something, she would call down to Pig.

When Pig wanted something, he would call up to all the others.

Yes, it was good to live this way.

Three in a tree!

One morning Cat wanted to sleep, but she couldn't.

Eagle was going in and out, in and out of the tree top.

Pig made funny noises from his home in the tree.

"How can I sleep here?" said Cat.

Up, up the tree she went.

"See here, Eagle!" said Cat.

"I think Pig is unhappy
with all this going in and out, in and out."

"If Pig is unhappy, why can't he
call up here and say so?" asked Eagle.

But Cat didn't answer.

She was on her way down the tree
to see Pig.

"What is it?" asked the pig
when he saw the unhappy face of Cat.

"Eagle does not like
the funny noises you make," said Cat.

"If Eagle is unhappy with me,
why can't he come down here and say so?"

But Cat did not answer.
She went on into the woods
to get something to eat.

NEW HOMES

Eagle and Pig were unhappy with Cat's news.

"Well," thought Eagle.

"I will not stay if I am not wanted."

And with that, he went away to another tree.

"I will not stay if I am not wanted," said Pig.

"I will find another tree."

And with that, he walked away to find another tree.

"Now I can get some sleep," Cat said.

Cat went back up the tree
to her home.

But when night came,
she couldn't sleep.

She was so unhappy!

"What are all the night noises?

Where are my friends, Eagle and Pig?"
she thought.

Cat missed her friends.

It was no fun being in a tree
without friends!

At last the morning sun came up, and Cat came down from the tree.

"I know what I have to do," she said. She ran into the woods to find her friends.

"I made up the things I said about you, Eagle," said the cat.

"And I made up the things I said about you too, Pig."

Eagle and Pig were surprised at this. But they still wanted to be friends with Cat.

So the eagle, the cat, and the pig went back to the tree.

Eagle went to the top.
Cat went to her home under Eagle.
Pig went to his home under Cat.

Three in a tree!
What a good way to live!

Paddy the Penguin

Paddy Wants to Fly

One morning Paddy was playing a game with the other penguins.

It was called "King of the Mountain."

In this game one penguin would be on top of a mountain of snow.

But the other penguins wanted to be on top too.

The penguin who could stay on top without being pushed off was called "King of the Mountain."

Paddy got to be King.

When Paddy was on top of the mountain of snow, he saw a white bird flying over him.

"How good it would be to fly like that," thought Paddy. "I know I can swim, but I would like to fly too."

All at once down went Paddy into the soft snow.

Another penguin had pushed Paddy when Paddy wasn't looking.

Now the other penguin was King of the Mountain.

Paddy *lay* on his back *in* the soft snow.

"What is that strange thing far up in the sky?" he thought.

It looked like a bird, but this one was not like other birds.

This bird did not have wings!

"A bird with no wings?" thought Paddy.

"How strange that a bird can fly when he has no wings!

If that bird can fly, then maybe I can fly too!"

Paddy got up
and walked away
from the other penguins.

He walked,

and

he

jumped,

and he swam,

and he walked some more.

Paddy did want to find
the strange bird.

Paddy and the Strange Bird

At last Paddy came to a little hill of snow.

He looked down.

The strange bird was there!

And with it was a big, big penguin!

The big penguin waved to Paddy.

Paddy came down from the little hill of snow.

He wanted a good look at the big penguin,

and at the bird

with no wings.

Then the big penguin did a strange thing.
He put something under Paddy's little wings.

"What is he doing?" thought Paddy.
"Could it be that he knows I want to fly?
Is this wise penguin doing something
that will help me fly?"

It was all so strange!

The big penguin helped Paddy get into the flying bird.

The bird made some strange noises, but then up into the sky it went.

And up went Paddy with it.

When the flying bird was far up in the sky, the big penguin came over to Paddy.

The big penguin pushed Paddy.

"Out you go!" he said.

And before Paddy could say "King of the Mountain," out he went.

"Where am I?" asked Paddy.

"What am I doing out here?"

Paddy was not in the flying bird.
He was out in the sky
over the mountains.

Paddy Penguin was flying!

Paddy looked up.
What was that strange thing
above him?

Paddy looked down. He could see
the other penguins looking up at him.

When Paddy came down into the soft snow,

all the other penguins walked over to him.

They all talked at once!

Paddy was so pleased!

Was he not a penguin who could fly?
Had he not seen the big, big penguin?
Had he not seen the bird with no wings?
Was he not King of the Mountain,

and King of the Penguins too?

Making and Choosing Words

Can you make words by putting the letters at the left of each row in the blanks? Write them on paper and see.

bl	____ack	____ond	____ast	____emp	____ame
ch	____air	____oke	____ep	____est	____ill
nd	se____	ba____	le____	ga____	wi____

What can people play?

a harp? a part? cards? barns? farms? barks?

Which ones can be seen?

a bark? a card? a yard? a harm? a mark?

Which can you do?

jump rope
tell a poke
eat a cone
poke a hole
hope for fun
jump up a pole
laugh at a joke
run home

Where Do Words Come From?

Did you ever stop to think about where words come from?

penguin—In Wales, *pen* means *white*, and *gwyn* means *head*. When men saw some new strange birds with white heads they called them *penguins*. Then, as time passed, men gave the same name to another bird. But this bird had a black head.

bonfire—This word was used long ago when people cooked meat in their houses and threw the bones outside. They did this all winter, and when spring came, they had a big bone fire. What is a bonfire today?

Do you know where these words came from? Ask someone to help you find out.

balloon **telephone**

5
MACHINES WORK FOR ALL

BUILDING A ROAD

It takes a long time to build a road.
Many workers and machines are needed.
First, men plan where the new road will go.
When the plans are finished,
other men
and machines
go to work.

A bulldozer is one machine that helps to build a new road.
A bulldozer can do the work of many, many people.

Shovels help build a road too.
They dig into the hills to get the dirt.

Big trucks carry the dirt away.
Over and over the trucks come to carry the dirt away.

A machine
with big round rollers works
on the new roadbed. This machine goes
over the roadbed many times.

One machine makes little rocks
out of big ones.
Many, many rocks are needed
to build a road.

The machine with the big round rollers
goes over the rocks.
Many, many times it goes up and down
over the rocks.

Another machine puts tar
on top of the rocks.
The roller machine comes back.
'Round and 'round
its rollers go
over the tar
and rocks.
Now the tar and rocks
will stay in place.

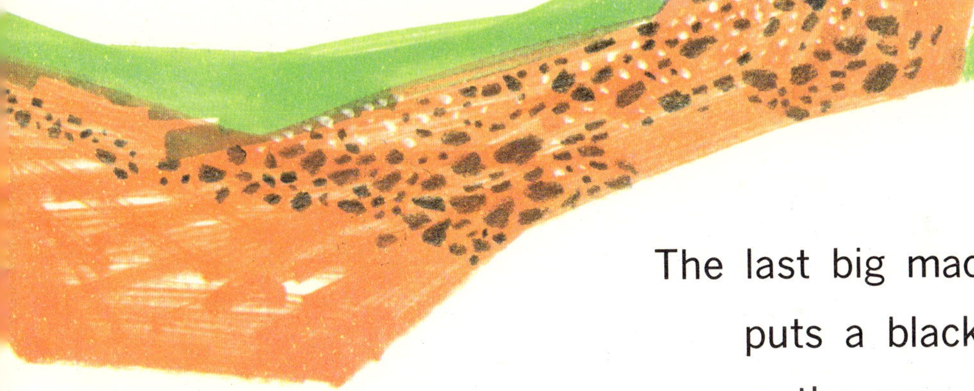

The last big machine
puts a black top
on the new road.
The road is finished, and soon
it will take people to many places.

Jeff's Mountain

Jeff lived in a little green house
on a country road.
On the other side of the road
was a mountain.
Jeff liked to look at his side
of the mountain.
When it was fair, with the sun
on the trees, the mountain was green.

At other times, when the sun went down, the mountain looked black. Sometimes it was white with snow.

Every morning on his way to school, Jeff would look up at the mountain. "How I wish I could go over that mountain," he thought. "I wish I could see what is on the other side."

Jeff liked to guess what it was like. But there was no road over the mountain. There was no way for Jeff to find out.

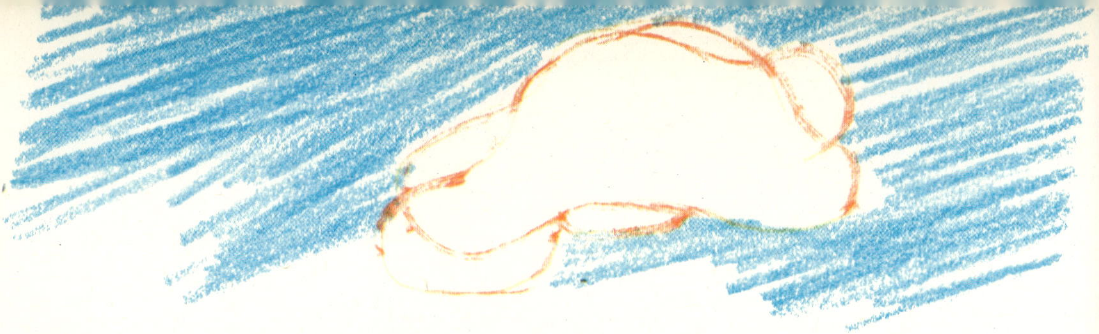

One morning a truck stopped
at Jeff's house. Some men got out of the truck.
One man put stakes into the road.
The other man looked at a big sheet of paper.
For a long time the men talked
and looked at the mountain.

"That's strange," Jeff thought.
"What are the stakes for?
What is on that sheet of paper?
Why are the men looking at the mountain?"

The man with the sheet of paper smiled at Jeff.
"What are you doing?" Jeff asked.

"We are going to build a road here," said the man.

"Will it go over the mountain?" Jeff wanted to know.

"Yes, it will," the man said.

"Boy, how I wish I could go over there," said Jeff. "What's on the other side?"

"You will see," said the man. "It will take a long time to build the road, but one day you can ride over the mountain.
Then you will see what's on the other side."

That day many men and machines
came to work on the new road.
For a long time Jeff watched
the truck and shovel and bulldozer at work.

Every day from then on, Jeff would run home
from school. He liked to watch
the men building the new road.

Jeff wished the men and machines
could work faster.
He couldn't wait to see
what was on the other side of the mountain.

A Long Time to Wait

Summer came,
and there was no school.
Every day Jeff watched the machines.
He liked to see the trucks come and go.
He liked the way the roller machine
rolled the rocks into place.
All the long summer days,
Jeff watched the road building.

Before long the summer was over.
Some of the trees on the mountain
were a blaze of red and yellow leaves.

Jeff watched a machine put tar
over the top of the road.
"Soon the road will be finished,"
he said. "Soon I will get my wish and see
what is on the other side of the mountain."

One winter morning when Jeff got up,
he looked out at the mountain.
The machines were not there.
The first snow of the winter
had come.
Everywhere it was white!

"Dad! Dad!" Jeff called.
"Where are the machines? Why did the workmen stop building the road?"

Jeff's dad looked up from his newspaper.
"Winter has come, Jeff," he said.
"The men can't work on the road now.
It says here in the paper that the men will go back to work in the spring."

"Spring!" said Jeff.
"But spring is so far off!
When will I find out what is on the other side of the mountain?"

Over the Mountain

The winter was long, but spring
came at last.
And with the first spring days
came the road workers.

In no time at all, the road
had its new black top.
There it was—a new road that went up
and over the mountain.

Jeff and his dad talked
about the new road.
Dad said that on Saturday
he would take Jeff for a ride
to see the other side
of the mountain.

Saturday came, and not too soon
for Jeff!
He couldn't wait to see
the other side of the mountain!

Up, up the mountain
went Dad's old car.
Jeff looked back.
How far away
the little green house looked from here!

Soon Jeff and his dad got to the top.
"Here we are," said Dad.
"Want to get out and take a look?"

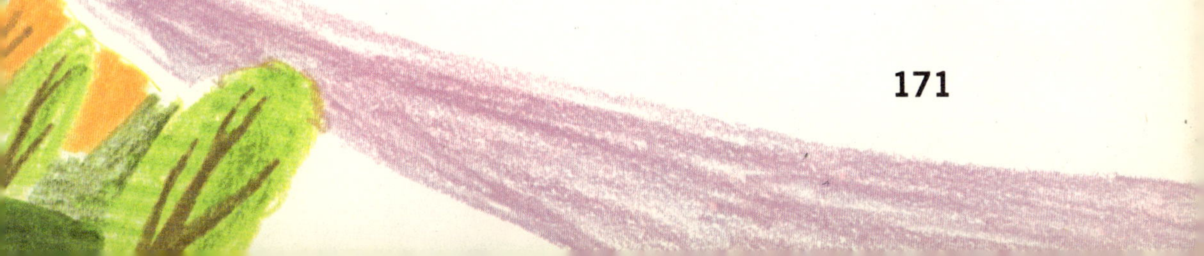

When Jeff got out of the car,
he saw a boy in a red cap watching him.
The boy waved and said,
"I came up here to see
what's on the other side
of the mountain."

"That's funny. So did I," said Jeff.

Then something surprised Jeff.
The boy with the red cap
was not looking the right way!
He was looking
down the side of the mountain
where Jeff lived.

"Look here," said Jeff.
"We each came up to find out
what was on the other side
of the mountain. But you are
not looking the right way.
I just came from that side.
I live there.
All you can find down there
is a little town."

The boy in the red cap looked at Jeff
in great surprise.
"But you are not looking the right way.
I just came from that side
of the mountain.
All that is down there
is a little town."

Jeff and the boy looked at each other.
How could each side of the mountain
be like the other?
The boys smiled, and then laughed.
"Well, I got my wish," said Jeff.

"I got my wish too," said the boy.
"And the road did something good for us.
Now you can ride over to my side,
and I can ride over to yours.
We will be friends.
THAT'S what is on the other side
of the mountain!"

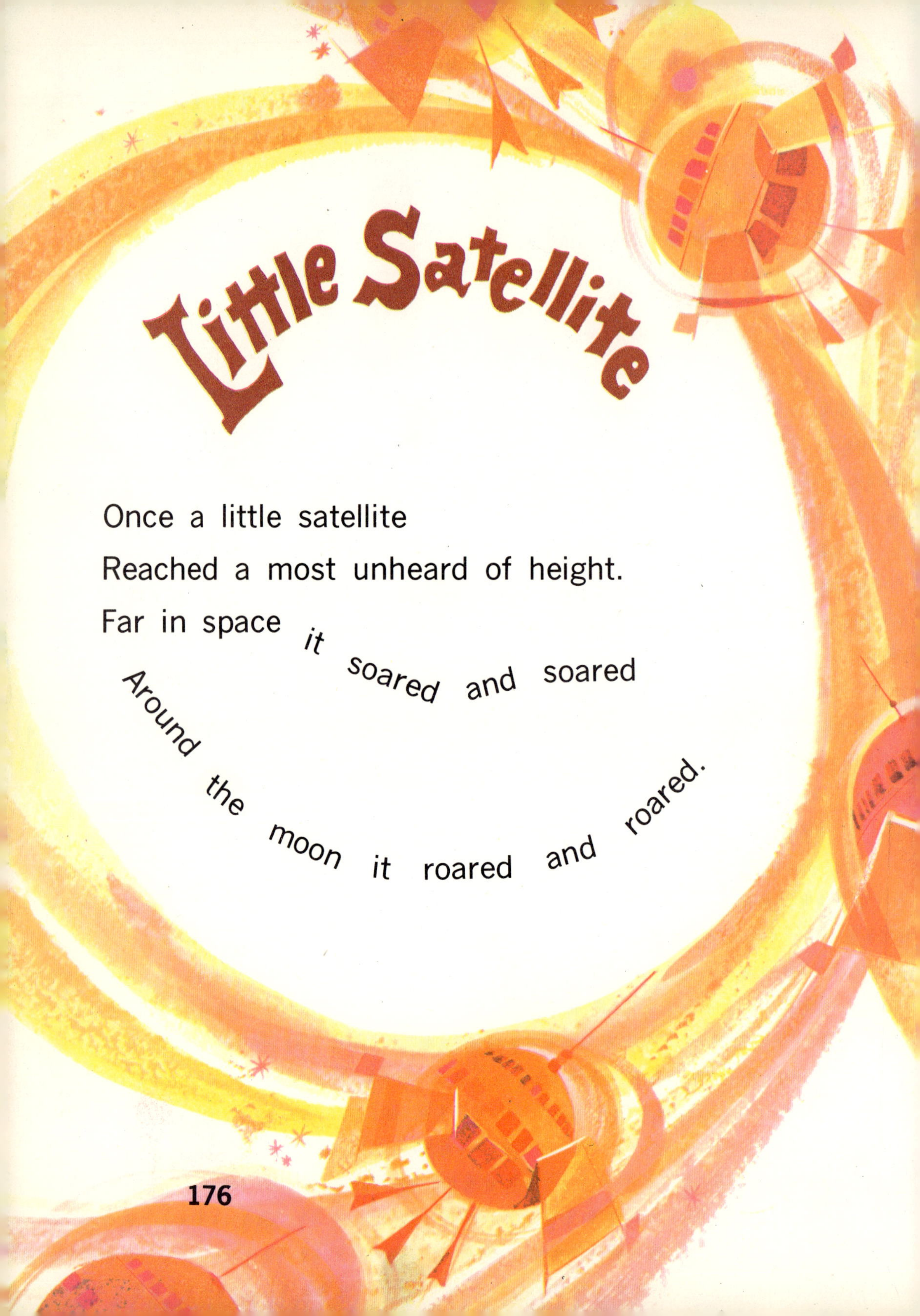

Little Satellite

Once a little satellite
Reached a most unheard of height.
Far in space it soared and soared
Around the moon it roared and roared.

Like a spinning, whirling base
Orbiting around in space
Beeping, beeping, all its worth
Messages sent back to earth.

What a trip for one so small,
Bravely speeding little ball.
Do you wish for earth again
When you're whirling in your spin?

Will you solve the mystery soon
Of outer space and of the moon?
I would only soar from sight
If I could return each night.

Jane W. Krows

Space Man

SCOT'S DREAM

It was Sunday night, and Scot was watching Space Man on TV.

Scot watched Space Man get into the rocket. Many times Scot had dreamed about being with Space Man.

"It would be fun if I could get into that rocket too," thought Scot. "It would be fun to go far out into space!"

That was the last thing Scot thought about. He had gone fast asleep before Space Man had finished his trip.

Scot began to dream.

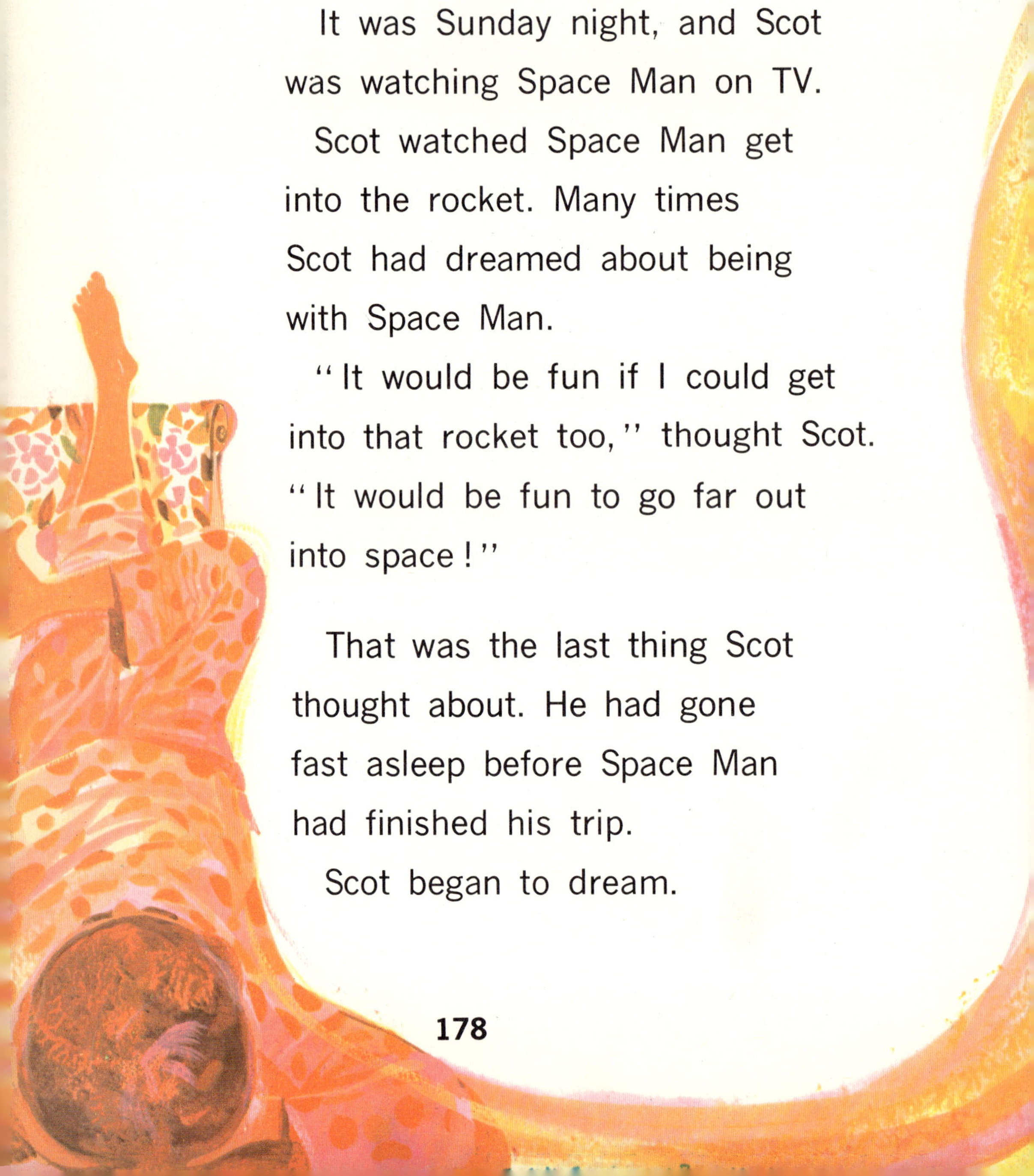

TO THE MOON

The time had come for Space Man Scot to go to the moon. He would be the first boy to land on the moon!

Scot walked outside, and looked up at the rocket. The rocket was as tall as seven houses! It was as tall as seven schools! This was the rocket that would take Scot to the moon.

Scot went inside the tall rocket.
Inside the rocket, men were
getting ready to blast off.

10 9 8 7 6 5 4 3 2 1

BLAST OFF!

Space Man Scot
began his trip to the moon!

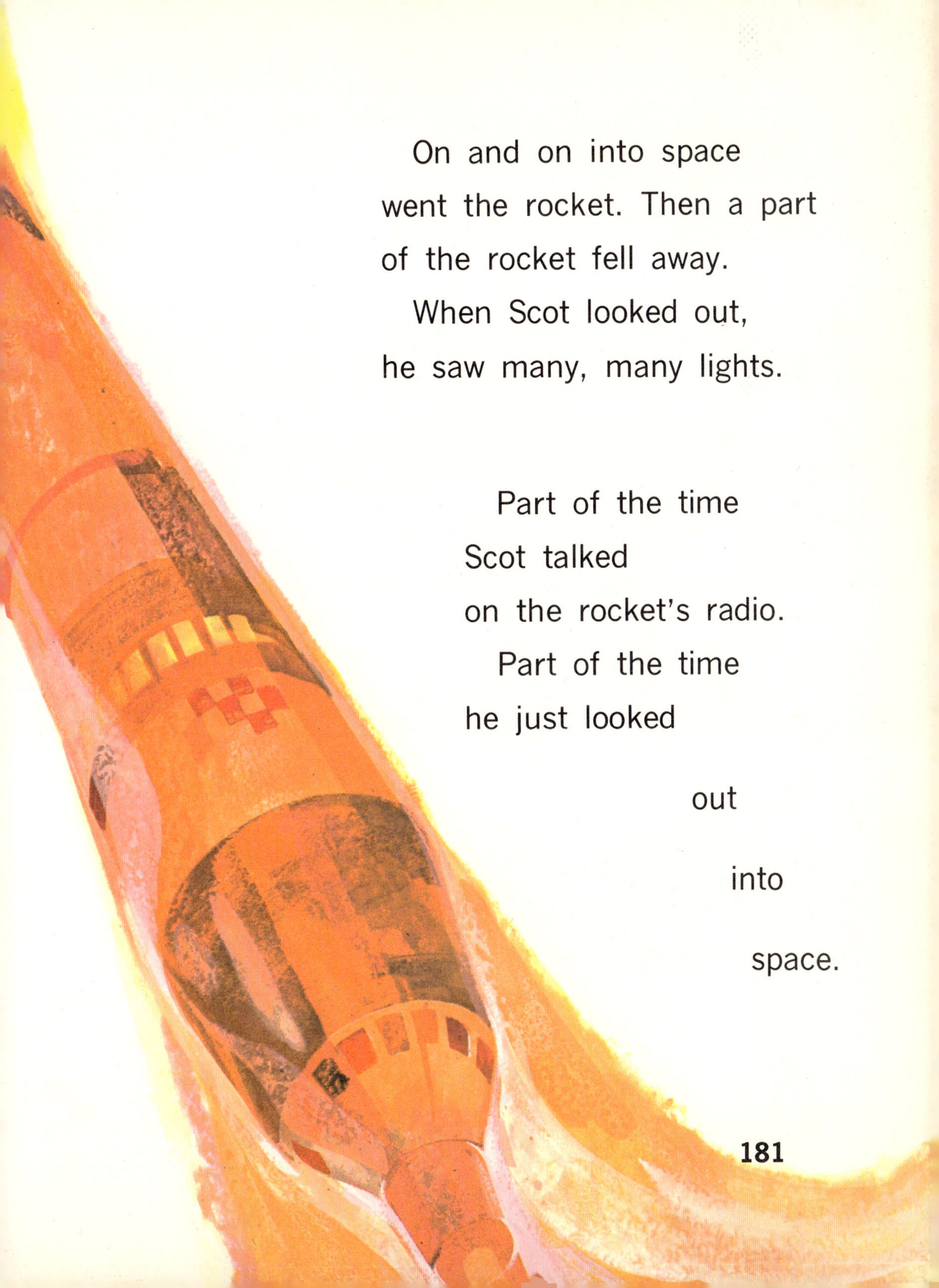

On and on into space
went the rocket. Then a part
of the rocket fell away.
When Scot looked out,
he saw many, many lights.

Part of the time
Scot talked
on the rocket's radio.
Part of the time
he just looked

out

into

space.

The rocket came to a stop at a Space Station. Some workers at the station took Scot inside.

They asked Scot to remember all the things he could about the trip.

Then the men talked with Scot about the other rocket that would take him on to the moon. They helped Scot get ready.

In the morning Scot and three of the men got into the moon rocket. Again they were ready to go.

10 9 8 7 6 5 4 3 2 1

BLAST OFF!

Away went the rocket with Scot and his friends inside. Away it went on its long trip to the moon.

ON THE MOON

At last the big rocket came to the moon. Scot and the men got out and looked around. What a strange place this was!

"Look here, Scot," said one man. "Do you see that big round thing that looks like a ball? You live on that ball. That's how your home looks from up here on the moon."

How strange it was for Scot to see that his home was on a big ball far out in space!

One man had a shovel. He wanted to take something from the moon back with him.

The other men walked around and talked on the radio.

Scot followed the men.

He was not looking where he was going, and he fell down.

Down
down
Scot
fell.

The dream was over,
and so was Scot's trip to the moon.

"Well!" said Mother.
"What are you doing down there?"

Scot laughed.
"I just fell off the moon!"
he said. "What a dream I had!"

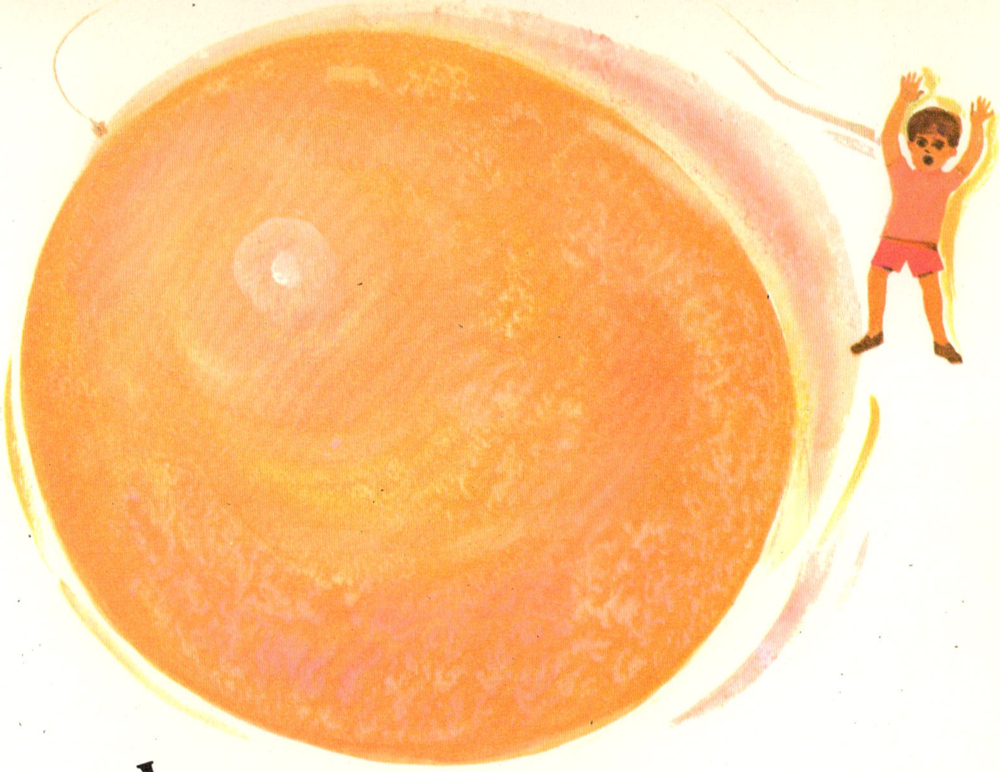

The Lost Balloon

A little boy
Was careless once,
  And lost his yellow
  Toy balloon.
It flew up high
And reached the sky
  And ever since
  It's called the moon.

Ilo Orleans

What Is in the Circle?

Read the words around the circle. Read the sentence in the circle. Think of a word that is like the other words and fits the sentence.

bid, bud, bad
You sleep in one.

pin, pen, pun
Your mother cooks in one.

went, sent, bent
You camp out in one.

stool, school, cool
A saw is one.

sheep, "cheep," weep
You do this at night.

band, land, sand
You have a right and a left.

back, black, sack
It is a small sharp thing.

shop, mop, stop
You do it on one foot.

book, look, shook
You can hang things on it.

Opposites

These words are opposites. Can you read them all?

Now draw pictures to show that these are opposites.

light	play	big	fast
dark	work	little	slow

Machines

Today we have many, many machines that can do wonderful things for us. Think about this morning when you got up.
How many machines did your mother use?
How many did your father use?
How about you?

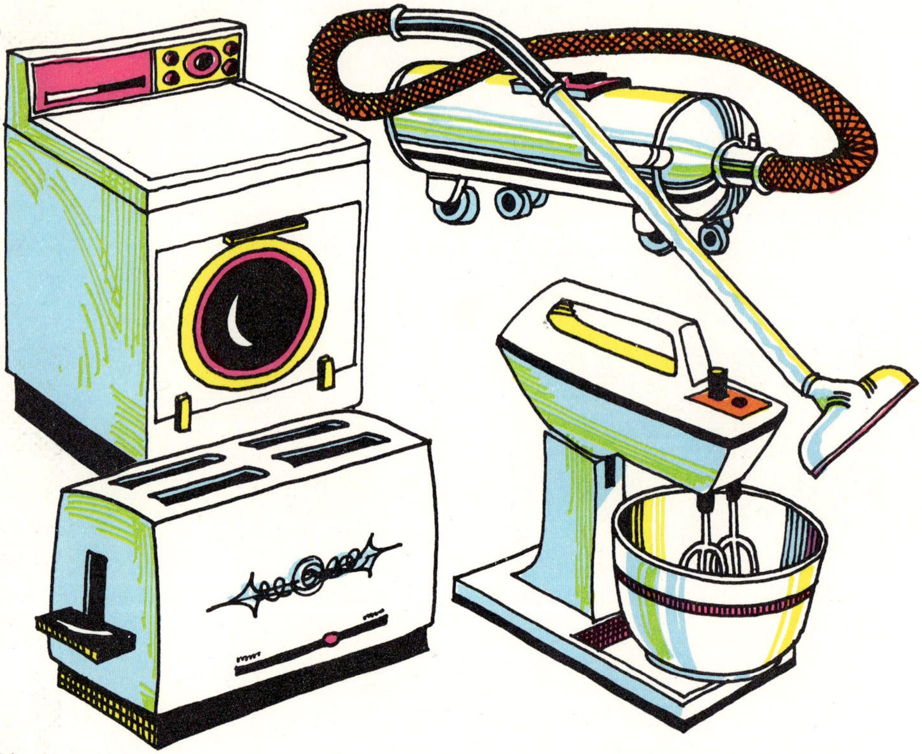

A boy once told his teacher that if he could build a new machine, it would be a homework machine.
If you could build a new machine, what would it do?
Can you draw a picture of it?
Can you write a story about it?

6
ONCE
LONG
AGO...

The Elves and the Shoemaker

The Shoemaker

A long, long time ago, a little old man and a little old woman lived in a little old house.

In the house there was a shop where the little old man made shoes. The little old woman helped him. They were happy when they had made many shoes.

One night the little old man said to the little old woman, "We have no money. We must have money to get the leather to make the shoes. We can't make shoes without leather. What can we do?"

The little old woman didn't like
to see the little old man so unhappy.
"Don't think about it now," she said.
"We can talk about the money
for leather in the morning."
So the little old man
and the little old woman went to bed.

In the morning the shoemaker came down into his store. There before him were seven new pairs of shoes.

"How can this be?" the shoemaker asked the little old woman. "Last night I had no leather to work with. Today I find seven new pairs of shoes! And they are well-made shoes too. How can this be?"

That day people came into the shoemaker's store. They liked the new shoes, and they gave the shoemaker money for them.

Late that day the old man went out to get more leather to make more shoes. When he got back, he didn't have time to make the shoes.

So the shoemaker went to bed.

When morning came, the shoemaker was surprised again.

"What's this?" he asked. "Again I find seven new pairs of shoes! How did they get here?"

Once more people came into the store for the shoes, and once more they gave the shoemaker money for them.

That night the old man talked with his wife.

"Tonight I won't go to bed," he said. "I'll stay up and see who comes to help me with my work."

"I'll stay with you," said the little old woman. "We'll watch and see who it is that works here for us."

The Helpers

Soon the little old man
and the little old woman
saw something strange.

Seven little elves came into the store.
The elves jumped about and sang.
Then they began to work on the shoes.
In no time at all they had made
seven new pairs of shoes.

"Do you see what I see?"
asked the little old man.
"The elves have no coats
and they have no shoes.
But they did all this work for us!"

"I think we can help them,"
said the little old woman.
"I will make seven coats for them.
And you can make seven little pairs
of shoes."

All the next day the little old man and the little old woman worked. They made seven little red coats and they made seven little pairs of red shoes.

"Let's hide and watch for the elves to come," said the shoemaker. So that is just what they did.

When the elves came that night, they were so surprised and happy! They liked the seven little red coats. And they were happy with the pretty red shoes.

The elves put on the new things and jumped around and sang.

"Thank you, old shoemaker," the elves called. "Thank you too, old woman. We helped you, for you are good people. We will not come again. Now you can make shoes without us."

And no one ever saw the little elves, not ever again.

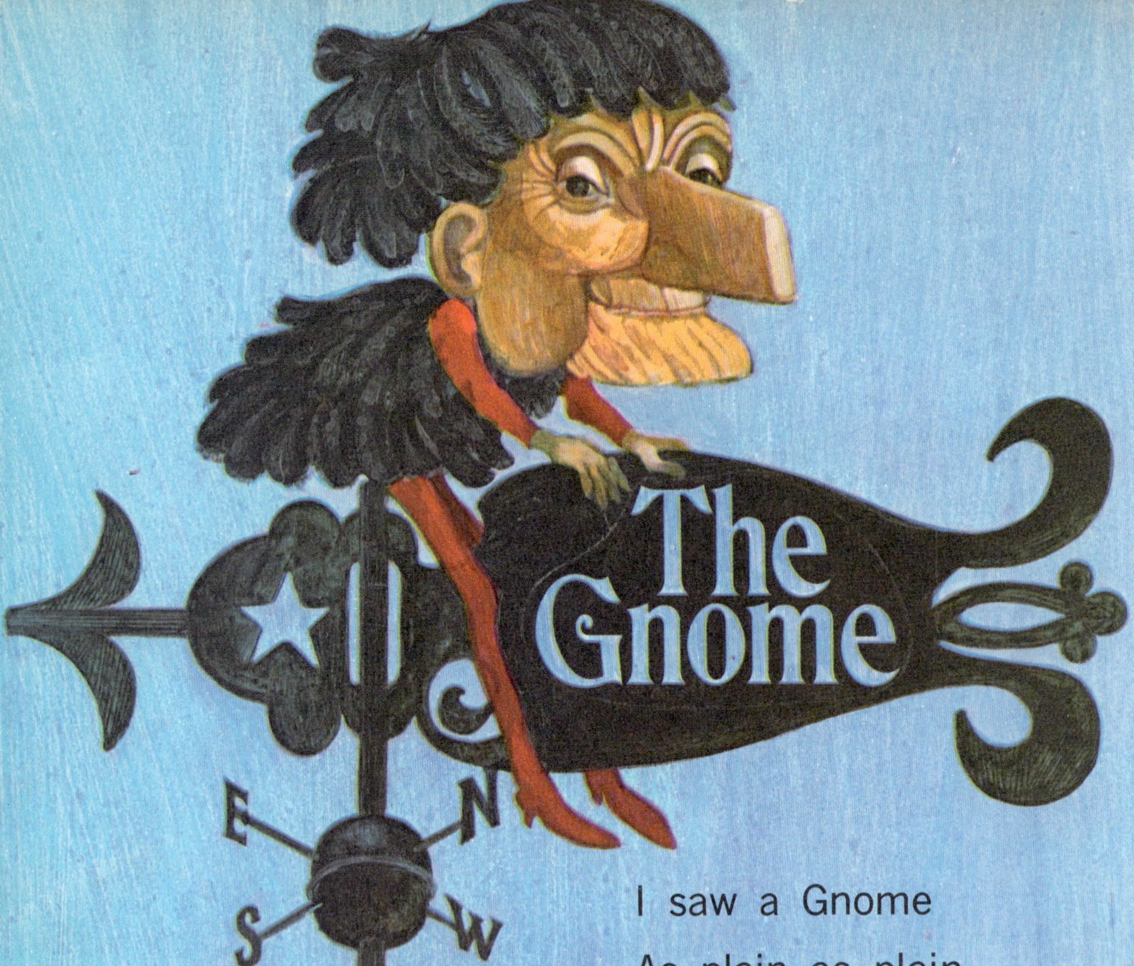

The Gnome

I saw a Gnome
As plain as plain
Sitting on top
Of a weathervane.

He was dressed like a crow
In silky black feathers,
And there he sat watching
All kinds of weathers.

He talked like a crow too,
Caw caw caw,
When he told me exactly
What he saw,

Snow to the north of him
Sun to the south,
And he spoke with a beaky
Kind of a mouth.

But he wasn't a crow,
That was plain as plain
'Cause crows never sit
On a weathervane.

What I saw was simply
A usual gnome
Looking things over
On his way home.

Harry Behn

THE BOY AND THE WOLF

*(An unhappy boy sits on a rock.
His sheep are all around him.)*

BOY: Why do I have to sit here
and watch the sheep? All day long
I just stay in this one place.
It is no fun being out here alone.

(Two men come up the hill.
The boy sees them.)

BOY: Help! Help! Please help me!
A wolf is going to eat my sheep!

FIRST MAN: Where? Where is the wolf?
Which way did he go?

BOY: Follow me!

(The men follow the boy
to the top of the hill.)

SECOND MAN: I see many sheep, but where is a wolf? Which way did the wolf go?

BOY: There is no wolf. I played a trick on you.

(The boy laughs.)

(The second man talks to his friend.)

SECOND MAN: This boy has tricked us.
Come, my friend. Let's get back
on our horses and ride into the city.
We have no time for this boy's tricks.

(The men ride down the hill.)

BOY: That was fun. I think I will do
it again.

(The boy runs and calls to the men.)

BOY: Help me! Help me!
A big wolf hides here by the tree.
This is no trick. The wolf is going
to eat my sheep!

FIRST MAN: Do you want to go back?
Maybe there is a wolf this time.

(The men ride up the hill again.)

SECOND MAN: There is no wolf here.
You have tricked us again.

FIRST MAN: But you will not play games
with us another time.
We are going,
and we will not come back.

(The men ride away.)

BOY: That was great fun.
The men thought the wolf
was going to eat my sheep!

(The boy laughs.)

I think I will just sit here
by the tree.

(The boy sits under the tree.)

(A wolf comes over the hill.)

WOLF: My, what beautiful white sheep you have! They look just right for eating!

(The boy jumps up.)

BOY: No! No! You can't eat my sheep!

WOLF: There is no one here to stop me. I can eat whatever I want. Which one will be the first?

(The boy runs to the top of the hill.)

BOY: Help! Help! Please help me! The wolf has come, and he is going to eat my beautiful sheep!

FIRST MAN: Playing tricks again, is he? What a strange boy he is! He can't trick us again. We know there is no wolf.

(The men ride on. The boy keeps calling.)

BOY: Please come! Please! This time there IS a wolf!

WOLF: You see? Now no one will help you. That is what you get for playing tricks!

White Horse

Long, long ago, many horses lived in the desert. There were red horses and gray ones. Some horses were all black. Others were black and white. And there was one beautiful white horse.

Indians lived here on the desert. They liked to catch the wild horses and ride them. They would make the wild horses work for them.

One day an Indian boy saw the beautiful white horse.

"Over here! Come here!" he called to his friends. "Just look at that beautiful horse! How I wish I could catch him!"

The other boys came over to see the beautiful horse.

"I think we can catch him for you," said the first boy. And with that, the boys jumped on their horses.

Fast as the wind went
the Indian boys on their horses.
Away over the desert they went.

Faster than the Indians went
the wild horses. Faster and faster they went,
and the white horse was first all the way.

Soon the wild horses became tired. They could run no longer. One by one the wild horses stopped.

But not the beautiful white horse. On and on he ran.

The Indian boys saw that the wild horses were tired. They saw that many of them had stopped.

One boy called out, "Faster! Ride faster! Soon we will get to the canyon. Then the white horse will have to stop. We can catch him by the canyon."

So the Indian boys went faster than ever. But the beautiful white horse went faster than all of them.

Now the boys could see the canyon.

"White Horse! White Horse! Stop! Stop!" called the boys.

But the beautiful white horse did not stop. Down, down he jumped. Down into the canyon jumped the beautiful white horse.

The Indian boys got off their horses and looked down into the canyon.

"Where can he be?" they asked, for the beautiful white horse could not be seen.

Then one boy called, "I see him! Look up there in the sky! There is the beautiful white horse!"

And if you are an Indian, you too, can see the white horse.

Up in the sky he runs, faster than the wind.

Silly Things to Read

On a sheet of paper write one of these silly sentences. Then draw a picture of it.

The bun will run and have fun in the sun.

The dog and the frog can jog with the log.

A mop can shop and hop with a top.

Ben and ten men saw a wet hen.

I see a wee bee near a green tree.

The tan can ran into Dan's pan.

I wish for a fish to swish in my dish.

I say Kay can play all day in May.

Two Make One

rail

road

→ railroad 

black

bird

→ blackbird 

snow

man

→ snowman 

bed

time

→ bedtime 

On your paper draw pictures of what the two words make when you put them together.

wish / bone

green / house

base / ball

watch / man

Where Do Our Stories Come From?

Long ago people did not understand how things came about. But they did ask questions. To answer such questions they made up their own stories. People told the stories to their children. Today we can read the stories that people made up long ago.

Indians told stories about the man in the moon.

Men long ago told stories about how the sun came to be in the sky.

Can you make up a story about how something might have happened? Maybe these questions will help you.

How did the stars get up into the sky?

What makes the wind blow?

What makes day and night?

Grandfather and I

Grandfather and I
are going for a walk.
It will be a slow walk
because
Grandfather and I
never hurry.
We walk along

and walk along

And stop . . .

And look . . .

just as long
as we like.

Other people we know
are always in a hurry.

Mothers hurry.

They walk in a hurry
and talk in a hurry.
And they always
want *you* to hurry.

But Grandfather and I
never hurry.
We walk along
and walk along

And stop . . .

And look . . .

just as long as we like.

Fathers hurry.
They hurry
off to work
and they hurry
home again.
They hurry
when they kiss you
and when they
take you for a ride.

But Grandfather and I
never hurry.
We walk along
and walk along

And stop . . .

And look . . .

just as long as we like.

Brothers and sisters
hurry, too.
They go so fast
they often bump into you.

And when *they* take you
for a walk
they are always
leaving you far behind.

But Grandfather and I
never hurry.
We walk along
and walk along

And stop . . .
And look . . .

just as long
as we like.

Things hurry . . .
Cars and buses,
trains and little boats.
They make noises
when they hurry—

They toot whistles
and blow horns.
And sometimes
scare you.

Grandfather and I never hurry.
We walk along and walk along

And stop . . .

And look . . .

just as long as we like.

And when Grandfather and I
get home
we sit in a chair
And rock and rock.
And sing a little . . .
And talk a little . . .
And rock and rock . . .
just as long as we like—

Until somebody
tells us to hurry.

• New Words in This Book •

The following new words are presented in *Seven Is Magic,* Level Six, Reading 360. Words printed in regular type are new basic words. Those underlined are enrichment words, and those printed in color are new words that pupils can decode independently.

UNIT I

PAGE	
6	Freckles
7	his
	face
8	shaving
	maybe
	cream
	him
10	other
	aren't
	shorty
	sometimes
	had
	smile
14	Pat's
	school
	picture
	took
	White
	thought
	about
15	day
16	children
17	Lucy's
18	her
	waved
	Cunningham
19	Dandy
	Mrs.
	well
23	seven
	magic
	wasn't
	birthday
	today
24	so
25	apartment
26	four
	brothers
	hamster
27	remember
29	telephone
	5th
	4th
30	o'clock
31	answer
32	grandmother
	please
	Andy
	fish
	milk
33	think
35	pork
	chops
	applesauce
	King
37	forgot
	forget
38	hadn't
	couldn't
39	right

UNIT II

44	fair
	steps
	Anders
	one
45	Bozo
	every
	would
46	postcard

47 mail
fun
could
49 woods
small
50 tags
tall
51 along
cut
logs
52 trucks
sawmill
pond
53 lumber
55 far
sky
weather
56 over
once
57 workers
hand
Sandy
58 instruments
59 radio
weathermen
parachute
62 Donna
roof
Don
64 lights
off
66 read (past tense)
67 air
schoolwork
68 Migs
long
before
letter
69 as
mailboxes
has
73 ago
sitting
fire
smoke
warm
held
first
74 basket
pan
75 more
rooster
sheep
76 fly

UNIT III

81 sights
82 Dan
bus
does
83 next
Saturday
you're
84 talked
many
happy
88 harbor
boats
everywhere
89 coming
90 noise
blue
91 someday
92 past
seen
95 softly
flakes
fell
soft
96 daylight
pretty
stay
97 keep
morning
98 snowballs
100 fence
Barry
around
we'll
your
workman
101 bad
everyone
us
103 seesaw
104 having

105 sun
Sam
hot
106 cool
108 water
wash
109 wet
splashed
or

UNIT IV

116 Goody
three
bird
117 sang
118 woke
sleepy
119 father
121 laughed
122 Harvey's
hat
wind
123 blew
124 farmer
stoplight
125 barn
blackbird
top
126 scarecrow
trick
127 left
soon
garden
128 stopped
129 an
130 unhappy
Bradford
Underwood
Timothy
Charles
Hoppenpopper
how
131 leave
great-grandfather's
grandfather's
been
wise
owl
132 paper
135 eagle
cat
139 another
140 friends
143 Paddy
penguin
game
mountain
pushed
145 lay
strange
wings
146 swam
150 above

UNIT V

156 road
needed
plan
157 bulldozer
shovels
dirt
dig
carry
158 round
roadbed
rollers
rocks
159 tar
place
black
160 side
Jeff's
161 wish
162 stakes
sheet
164 watched
faster
165 summer
rolled
166 blaze
167 winter
168 newspaper
spring
172 cap
173 each
178 Scot's

dream
Sunday
rocket
TV
asleep
gone
began
179 moon
land
outside
180 inside
ready
blast
181 part
183 station
again

UNIT VI

192 elves
shoemaker
shop
shoes
money
must
leather
194 pairs
195 gave
196 wife
tonight
won't
I'll
197 helpers
198 coats
201 ever
204 wolf
sits
alone
205 two
which
second
206 our
horses
208 by
209 beautiful
whatever
211 desert
gray
212 Indians
catch
wild
213 their
than
214 became
tired
longer
canyon

LIST OF ILLUSTRATORS

Tom Cooke
Lois Ehlert
John Kuzich
Jane Teiko Oka
Logan Holtby
Fred Witzig
Donald Silverstein
Richard Powers
Albert John Pucci
Franz Altschuler
David M. McPhail

DEFGHIJ 7654321
PRINTED IN THE U.S.A.